Two is a Line

by Jon Madian

Photographs by

Lou Jacobs Jr.

Platt & Munk, Publishers/New York

David and Mike both want
to use the swing.
The boys shout, ''It's my turn!''
They push each other.

The teacher comes between them.
She asks, "Are you fighting
for a turn on the swing?"
"Yes," the boys answer.
The teacher says, "While you fight
neither of you can use the swing."

David and Mike look at the empty swing.
Maybe the teacher is right.

They sit down with the teacher.
She asks, "How can you tell whose turn
it is without fighting?"

The boys think very hard.
Then Mike says,
"I know. We can make a line."

"Very good idea," says the teacher.
"Two is a line. One in front and one in back."

Karen wants to play on the swing, too.
She gets in line in back of David.
Soon it will be her turn.

Mike goes first.

He swings higher and higher.

Then it is David's turn.
David makes the swing spin around and around.

Karen puts her
head way back.

Everything looks
upside down.

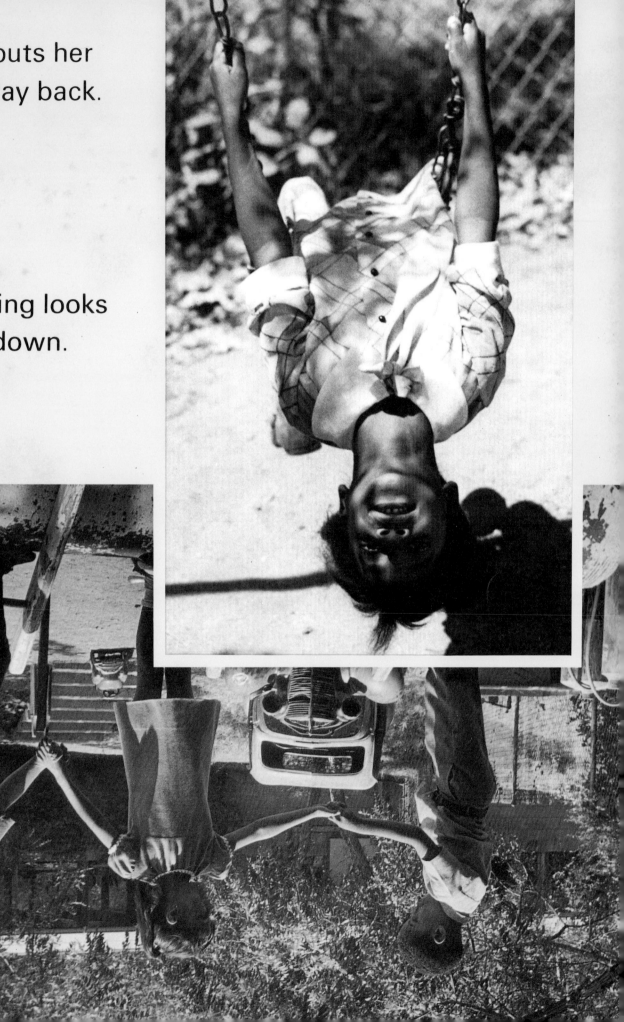

The children have fun taking turns.
"Let's take our line to the slide," Mike says.

Linda comes over and says, "I want to go on the slide."
Karen stops her. "Wait!" she says. "We have a line.
You have to get in line behind me."

Linda wants to slide right away.
But she knows it is not her turn yet.
She waits at the end of the line.

Karen looks down at the line.

"Our line is getting longer," she says.

"There are one, two, three, FOUR in our line."

Karen slides down the slide.

Now it's Linda's turn.

Linda says, "I like our line because now I'm first."

The children are thirsty. They run over
to the water fountain and make a new line.

Then they run to the car.
They get in line to drive it.
Gary wants to drive the car, too.
He tries to push his way into the front of the line.

David tells Gary he must wait.
"We have a line!
Get behind Karen and soon it will be your turn."

"Why do I have to be last in line?" asks Gary.
The teacher tells him, "Everyone has to be last in line for a short time."
Karen says, "Our line has really grown.
Now we have FIVE children in the line."

After the children have driven the car,
Gary says, "Let's play fire trucks.
We can be a line of fire trucks going to a fire."

Then everyone holds the hose.

David says, ''Look! We're a line of five firemen.''

When the fire is out, the children
take their line to the jungle gym.
David climbs up and looks down
at the line of children.
''Hey, come on up!'' he shouts.
''Everyone can play on the jungle gym.''

The children laugh as they climb
all over the jungle gym.
There is room for everyone.
They do not need a line now.